Beatrix Pot... Bunnyk...

Price Guide

Doug Pinchin (Text)
Nick Tzimas (Listings)
Trevor Leek (Photography)

Francis Joseph Publications
ISBN 1 870703 66 9

© Francis Joseph Publications 1995

First impression

Published in the UK by
Francis Joseph Publications
15 St Swithuns Road, London SE13 6RW

Typeset and printed, in Great Britain by
E J Folkard Print Services
199 Station Road, Crayford, Kent DA1 3QF

ISBN 1 870703 66 9

Contents

Acknowledgements

Doug Pinchin has been involved with Doulton Wares for over twenty years, first as a collector and for the last sixteen years as a dealer and writer.

He has written many articles for collectors magazines, notably the Royal Doulton International Collectors Club magazine and *Collecting Doulton* of which he is now editor. Doug is currently working on a new edition of the *Doulton Figures Collectors Handbook* to be published by Francis Joseph in 1996 and *Doulton Figures as a Reflection of Time* in collaboration with Jocelyn Lukins.

Nick Tzimas Managing Director of UKI Ceramics Limited published the first reference books on Bunnykins and Beatrix Potter and the company has at present a ten year contract with Royal Doulton to produce exclusive limited edition Bunnykins figures. Nick has drawn from his knowledge and experience in the past 15 years to produce a comprehensive pricing guide to all the Bunnykins and Beatrix Potter figures which reflects the average market availability. It is based on auction results, dealer asking and buying prices and the rarity value of each item.

Trevor Leek A studio photographer for over ten years, Trevor works from Greenwich in south-east London, and has photographed collections all over the country. He has produced work for Francis Joseph ever since the first editions of *The Character Jug Collectors Handbook* came out in 1983.

No book on Beatrix Potter or Bunnykins figures is possible without mention of Louise Irvine's pioneering research on the subject. The author is also indebted to her for permission to use certain material regarding Beatrix Potter's early attempts to produce figurines of her characters.

Introduction: The Rise and Rise of Bunnykins and Beatrix Potter Figures

Bunnykins to the Fore

The collectables market is fickle but during the last twenty years or so the name of Royal Doulton has consistently ranked high in the collectability stakes. The enthusiasm for the miriad of ceramics produced by the company shows no sign of failing. Even within the world of collecting Royal Doulton fashions change. The causes of these changes are as difficult to define with Royal Doulton as with any other product. What is certain is that Royal Doulton items hold some special magic for collectors and while, say, character jugs may not be so popular this year their time will come again. Traditionally, figurines, character jugs, series ware and Lambeth pottery are the most popular Doulton collectables but in the last five years their pole position has been challenged. The challenge has come from an unexpected and hitherto comparatively neglected area of Royal Doulton's activity – Bunnykins figures.

For many years there have been collectors of Bunnykins tableware, however the cute little rabbits which initially evolved from the characters depicted on the plates and cups and saucers had been largely ignored by adult collectors. They had remained confined to the nursery. This was after all their intended destination. So what caused Bunnykins collectors to multiply like, well, rabbits? It is not easy to be certain what caused this surge of interest but there are a couple of factors which might have played a part. The first was the commissioning of the Bunnykins Collectors Band by U.K. Fairs Ltd. This was a colourway of the Bunnykins Oompah Band which was made in a limited number of 250 sets and only available at the U.K. Doulton Collectors Fair in October 1990. The edition was sold out on the day. The success of the Band caused considerable interest in the Doulton world. Collectors became Bunnykins aware. U.K. Fairs and its sister company, U.K. International Ceramics, spurred on by the strength of the somewhat unexpected interest in Bunnykins figures commissioned further limited editions. The Bunnykins Royal family in a new colourway came next followed by a range of new characters all in limited editions. Around the world special Bunnykins commissions for specific markets ensured that the Bunnykins figure phenomenon became international.

The other factor which may have fuelled the take-off of Bunnykins figures is the behaviour of Royal Doulton itself. Bunnykins figures in their present form were introduced in 1972. By 1974 there were still only fifteen models in the range and no more characters were added until 1982. Neither were there any withdrawals during this period. By 1985 the range had more than doubled. No doubt the 50th Anniversary celebrations of Bunnykins tableware in 1984 had helped things along. The pace of introductions quickened during the mid 1980's, but only a handful of models were discontinued. However in 1987-88 a significant number of figures were withdrawn, almost instantly transforming them into secondary market collectables.

The combination of 'special' Bunnykins figures becoming available and a number of 'standard' Bunnykins figures becoming unavailable may have caused the spark that ignited the market. It is impossible to be certain of the reasons but it is undeniable that Bunnykins figures together with Beatrix Potter figures have become two of the leading collectables of the 90's.

The Beatrix Potter Figure Phenomenon

Unlike the Bunnykins Characters which were largely the brain-child of the ceramics industry, the Beswick Beatrix Potter figures have a much longer pedigree. It is just over one hundred years since Beatrix Potter wrote an illustrated letter to a sick child about the adventures of a rabbit called Peter and over ninety years since her original stories were first commercially published. Every generation since has fallen under the spell of her characters and their adventures. From 1948 enthusiasts could purchase ceramic models of Peter Rabbit and his friends produced by the Beswick pottery. The little figures, closely and accurately modelled on Beatrix Potter's drawings were an immediate success and have remained so ever since, surviving the takeover of Beswick by Royal Doulton in 1969 and the change of brand name to Royal Albert in 1989.

In recent years the already strong interest in the stories and characters of Beatrix Potter has grown to huge proportions. All manner of Beatrix Potter merchandise is now available. Everything from bed-linen to postage stamps has been produced featuring the familiar characters. The centenary of the first Peter Rabbit story in 1993 and the resulting promotional activity added to the public's awareness of Beatrix Potter's work. As could be expected, the popularity of the Beswick/Royal Albert figures also flourished. The demand for more information resulted in the publication of a flood of books, not only about Beatrix Potter and her stories but also about the figures. Initially a chapter in the *Beswick Collectors Handbook* by Harvey May listed, for the first time, all the Beswick Beatrix Potter figures and then five years later in 1992 *Beatrix Potter Figures* edited by Louise Irvine was devoted solely to the whys and wherefores of collecting the figures and their associated products. As so often happens with the publication of a specialised book, even more more collectors were brought into the market. Armed with new information the search was on for the elusive discontinued models as collectors strived to complete their collections.

How This Book Will Help You

It is indisputable that there are many similarities in the appeal of Royal Doulton Bunnykins figures and Beswick/Royal Albert Beatrix Potter figures. They may have sprung from a different area of inspiration but in today's collectables market they are inexorably linked. It is not unusual to find that collectors enthusiastically collect both ranges. The market for both continues to go from strength to strength. In addition to providing a complete listing of both ranges, (in alphabetical order) it is also the intention of this book to help collectors gain an insight into a sometimes bewildering aspect of collecting – pricing.

Each entry is given a price in the form of a range of values the collector might expect to pay for the figure on the open market. However the old maxim that something is only worth what someone is prepared to pay for it holds true but faced with an ever growing number of discontinued models it is helpful to have a guide to the general market value of a piece. In the final analysis the collector must decide if the asking price is acceptable to him. If the answer is 'yes' then that is the true value of the item.

Bunnykins and Beatrix Potter figures are no longer solely the province of young collectors. Adults and children alike have fallen under their enchantment. Could it be that we are really all still children at heart?

Doug Pinchin

Benjamin ate a Lettuce Leaf P3317 and Peter and the Red Pocket Handkerchief P3242.

The Story of Beatrix Potter Figures

Beatrix Potter was born in London in 1866 to well-to-do middle class parents. She was considered to be a delicate child and educated at home by a series of governesses. Her rather solitary existence was enlivened by a talent for drawing which showed itself at an early age. Luckily for future generations this talent was encouraged by her parents. Her early models were the assortment of pets she and her younger brother accumulated. Family holidays in the Lake District and Scotland stimulated her interest in the natural world which she recorded in paintings and drawings. When away from London Beatrix would write letters to the children she knew, many of which were the children of her former governesses. One such letter sent on 4th September 1893 was to prove rather important. The recipient was five year old Noel Moore. The letter was an attempt to cheer up Noel who was ill and told the story of a rabbit called Peter. Evidently the letter pleased Master Moore because he still had it eight years later. Beatrix borrowed back the letter intending to turn it into a book. She was unable to find a publisher but undaunted she had 250 copies printed privately which she sent to family and friends for Christmas 1901. In the meantime she continued to search for a commercial publisher. The search ended in 1902 when an agreement was reached with Frederick Warne and Co. The book was reillustrated in colour and published in October1902 in an edition of 8,000 copies. Within a matter of months 28,000 copies were printed.

The Tale of Peter Rabbit was followed in 1903 by *The Tale of Squirrel Nutkin*. For the next few years an average of two new books a year were published. Also at this time the first Beatrix Potter character merchandise appeared which included a board game, wall paper designs and a Peter Rabbit soft toy.

Beatrix Potter's editor at Frederick Warne was Norman Warne. They developed a close relationship and in 1905 Norman proposed. Beatrix's parents did not approve but nevertheless she accepted. However the marriage was not to be. Norman died suddenly only a few weeks later. Naturally heartbroken Beatrix turned to her work for comfort, producing three

Peter Rabbit Soft Toy made by Steiff in Germany in 1905. It was evident from her later dealings with ceramic companies Beatrix Potter was very demanding when producing her creations, implying no British manufacturer met her standards. It is made from lambswool plush stuffed with thin strips of wood. (Courtesy of Clive Corless, reproduced by permisison of BBC Homes and Antiques)

more books. She also bought a property in the Lake District where she spent more and more of her spare time, the countryside providing the background for many of her books. Family committments eventually brought her back to London but she continued to produce her books – eleven more in seven years.

The royalties from her books allowed Beatrix to buy more properties in the Lake District. In the course of doing this she met a local solicitor, William Heelis. On 15th October 1913 they were married. The Lake District became her home and farming her life. Only five more books were written. Beatrix Potter died on 22nd December 1943. By now her Lake District estate amounted to 4,000 acres which she left to The National Trust.

The First Attempts to Produce Beatrix Potter Figures

It can be seen from the earliest days of her success that Beatrix Potter felt that there was scope for her creations to be lifted off the printed page and into other marketable products. There was an attempt around 1907 to produce ceramic models of her characters. She had modelled some clay figures and had contacted Royal Doulton's Lambeth pottery with a view to having them reproduced. Nothing came of this project as there was already an agreement with a German firm to make a range of nurseryware based on her characters. Miss Potter did not like the German product and attempts were made to cancel or alter the agreement. About ten years later there was another abortive attempt to make Beatrix Potter character figures.

A Stoke on Trent firm, Grimwades, sent Beatrix a model of Jemima Puddle-Duck. She did not approve of it but was interested enough to pursue the matter a little more. She sent to the factory some clay figures she had modelled herself. It is not clear if these were the same figures she had taken to Royal Doulton. The figures were damaged in transit but enough survived to allow Grimwades to see what she had in mind. Another model of Jemima Puddle-Duck was made which Beatrix liked better. However this time she did not like the colouring. It was then suggested that there could be some sort of co-operation between Grimwades and Royal Doulton who had more experience in colouring figures. It is recorded that Beatrix liked this idea but nothing came of it. It would seem that Royal Doulton was destined to become involved in producing Beatrix Potter figures but the final connection was still some years away and only happened after Beatrix Potter had died and even then as a result of a factory take-over.

Beswick Beatrix Potter Figures

It was another Stoke on Trent pottery which finally succeeded in producing the first acceptable range of Beatrix Potter figures. The Beswick factory was founded in 1894. Initially it manufactured domestic wares in both china and earthenware but became most well known for its animal models and novelties. The idea to create a range of Beatrix Potter figures came from Lucy Beswick, wife of the chairman and Managing Director of the company. Mrs Beswick was born in Cumbria and the family often returned to the Lake District for holidays. It was on one of these visits that Mrs. Beswick visited the home of Beatrix Potter. On returning to the potteries she suggested to the company's chief modeller, Arthur Gredington, that Jemima Puddle-Duck would make an attractive figure. A suggestion from the chairman's wife was obviously not one to be ignored and a clay model was duly produced. Having secured the approval of Mr. Beswick and the other directors, and copyright permission obtained from Frederick Warne and Co., further characters were modelled. The first collection consisted of ten of the most popular characters. Jemima Puddle-Duck, Peter Rabbit, Tom Kitten, Timmy Tiptoes, Squirrel Nutkin, Mrs. Tittlemouse, Little Pig Robinson, Benjamin Bunny, Samuel Whiskers and Mrs. Tiggywinkle. Great care was taken to be true to the original illustrations both in terms of modelling and colouring.

The figures were ready in 1948 but because war-time restrictions on the sale of decorative china in the home market, the figures had to be launched abroad. The reaction from customers was tremendous, with much comment on how accurately they had been transferred from the printed page. More models were added to the collection but it was not until 1977 that all the Beatrix Potter tales had contributed characters. The first figure was discontinued in 1967. This was, of course, the 1955 introduction **Duchess** (P1355) which now commands a noteworthy price on the secondary market.

Royal Doulton Take Over

The Beswick company was sold to Royal Doulton in 1969 but the Beatrix Potter figures continued to be marketed under the Beswick backstamp until 1989 when they were transferred to Royal Albert. To those outside the Royal Doulton group this move was perceived as a little odd as Royal Albert had hitherto been best known for its range of rather flowery and ornate tableware. No doubt Royal Doulton had its reasons but to the best of my knowledge they have never made them public. Nevertheless after the previous failed attempts Royal Doulton has, since 1969, been responsible for producing ceramic Beatrix Potter figures albeit under a different name. No doubt Miss Potter would finally approve.

Other Items are Added to the Collection

The success of the figures spawned other Beatrix Potter ceramic items. The first to appear was a lamp base in the shape of a tree. This was sold on its own or with a choice of figure. The wood theme was continued in 1970 when a display base for six Beatrix Potter figures was introduced. It is modelled in the form of gnarled and knotted wood.

On two occasions Beswick produced wall plaques featuring Beatrix Potter characters. The first time was in 1967 when three subjects were modelled, the plaque taking the form of the character. They only remained in production for two years but in 1977 another three subjects were tried, this time as relief moulded square plaques. Again they only met with limited success.

More success was achieved with the introduction in 1989 and 1990 of a set of six character jugs based on Beatrix Potter characters. Attractive and charming though they undoubtedly are, one cannot help wonder what Miss Potter might have thought of this concept, bearing in mind her concern over the original attempts to produce ceramic figures.

Another short-lived experiment was the collection of Studio Sculptures introduced in 1984 and 1985. These were seven Beatrix Potter characters modelled in great detail and cast in a 'bonded ceramic' body at the John Beswick Studios. They failed to capture the collectors imagination and were withdrawn from production at the end of 1985. Even today they are generally not considered to be part of the usual Beatrix Potter collection.

Proving to be more popular is the range of tableware and giftware decorated with Beatrix Potter characters which was introduced in 1987 and is still available today. These were the first Beatrix Potter items to carry the Royal Albert backstamp.

Since 1989 when Royal Doulton transfered the Beatrix Potter figures from the Beswick backstamp to Royal Albert it would seem logical that all new issues should carry the Royal Albert mark. In 1993 to celebrate the centenary of Peter Rabbit a new large size version of Peter was issued which for that year only had a special commemorative Beswick backstamp. From 1994 onwards it would become Royal Albert. Peter Rabbit was joined in the Royal Albert range by two further large size figures, Jeremy Fisher and Tom Kitten. It would appear that Royal Doulton became rather fond of centenary celebrations as 1994 saw the hundreth anniversary of the founding of the Beswick company. It was marked by the issue of a large size version of Jemima Puddle-Duck which for one year only would carry the Beswick backstamp before changing to Royal Albert. Royal Doulton predicted that 'this special Beswick item will no doubt prove hugely popular amongst collectors and Beatrix Potter lovers alike'. Currently the range of large size figures stands at eight. Foxy Whiskered Gentleman, Mrs. Rabbit and the Tailor of Gloucester having been added to the Royal Albert collection.

To date only the lamp base, the character shaped wall plaques and to some extent the character jugs have joined the figures as being really collectable. No doubt if the enthusiasm for Beatrix Potter's work continues to grow, and there is no reason to suppose it will not, the other items will eventually take off and become highly prized collectables.

When she wrote and illustrated that first letter to Master Moore could Beatrix Potter have imagined what she had created?

How Bunnykins and Beatrix Potter Figures are Made

Bunnykins and Beatrix Potter figures are made in the same way at the same factory. Even though they carry different backstamps, Royal Doulton and Beswick or Royal Albert respectively, both ranges are made at Royal Doulton's John Beswick factory at Longton, Stoke on Trent.

The one real difference is one of source. All the Beatrix Potter figures are taken from Miss Potter's original illustrations while Bunnykin figures spring from the imaginations of Royal Doulton's team of designers and just occasionally an outside artist.

If it is a Beatrix Potter figure that is to be created the in-house designer will study the original illustration of the character and generally familiarise themselves with the character. He will then produce reference drawings for the modeller, filling in the necessary details to turn a one dimentional illustration into a three dimentional model. In the case of a Bunnykins figure the designer will work from a design brief or perhaps his own ideas. The modeller and the designer work together to produce a clay model of the proposed figure. Assuming that the model is not rejected at this point, a set of plaster of Paris master moulds will be made. How many moulds depends on the complexity of the figure. Usually a Bunnykins figure needs a seven part mould, three parts for the head and four parts for the body. The original clay model is cut into pieces to allow the moulding to take place. This is a very skilled job as mistakes cannot easily be rectified. Three or four figures are cast from these moulds for colour trial and approval.

It is undesirable to cast too many figures at this stage. If the model is passed for production, and some are rejected at this stage, the mould has to be used again to make the rubber case from which the working moulds will be made. Over use will result in a blurring of the detail in the figure. With Beatrix Potter figures the trial pieces have to be approved by the copyright holders to ensure that the figure is true to the original illustration.

Once approval is received and the working moulds made, production can commence. Both Bunnykins and Beatrix Potter figures are cast in earthenware in liquid form known as slip. The slip is poured into the assembled mould through a hole in the top. Some of the moisture in the slip is absorbed by the Plaster of Paris moulds and a crust or skin is formed on the inside of the mould. When the required thickness is achieved, the excess slip is poured away and the mould carefully dismantled. The constituent parts are then assembled using more slip to 'glue' them together. The resulting joins are sponged smooth, a process known as fettling. The figure is extremely fragile and it takes great skill not to damage it during handling. After being allowed to dry out the figure is ready for its first firing. The kiln is heated to 1200 deg. C. which dries out any moisture left in the body. This results in a shrinkage of about 1/12th of the figure's original size. The figure is now at what is known as the biscuit stage and ready for decoration.

Working from an approved completed figure the painters now apply under glaze ceramic colours. The paint is fired on during a second firing at the lower temperature of 760 deg. C. On emerging from the kiln the figure is allowed to cool before being dipped in liquid glaze. It is then fired once more, this time at just over 1000 deg. C. The figure comes out of the kiln in its finished form. Occasionally, when there is a need for special colours some on-glaze colours are added. These too need to be fired on but at a much lower temperature. The red of Santa Bunnykins suit is an example of on-glaze colours being used.

Each completed figure is then inspected for imperfections as Royal Doulton insist that quality control is extremely strict. Then the perfect figures start their journey to collectors around the world . . .

No More Twist P3325 Hunca Munca Spills the Beads P3288.

Rarities and Oddities

For some collectors there is always an appeal in having something different or unusual. Over the years there have been many changes in modelling and colouring within the Beatrix Potter figure collection and so there is scope to assemble a collection of unusual pieces. Of course these rarities will carry a price premium. So far, however, the Bunnykins figure collection has remained more or less unchanged with regard to this sort of alteration and so the market for variations of standard models has not developed

Bunnykins Figures

With one or two exceptions the Bunnykins figures which can be considered as rare are those which were, quite simply, produced in limited numbers. The Bunnykins figures introduced in 1939 are scarce because the outbreak of war ended the production of most decorative ceramics. Consequently their production span was very short and over the subsequent years breakages will have reduced their number still more. The same is true of the bunny-shaped tableware introduced at the same time. It is not surprising that pieces bought in 1939 for a few shillings are now worth hundreds, if not thousands, of pounds.

Of the more recent Bunnykins figures it is largely the various limited editions which have become more difficult to find and therefore more expensive. Leading the way is Collector Bunnykins but some of the colourways produced for special events in the United States are also very elusive.

There are only a few colour changes to be considered. Over the years slight variation in the colouring of certain figures has occured but the differences are so slight as to make no change to the value of the piece. William Bunnykins has been found with an unpainted white jacket which obviously changes his appearance and could increase the value of the figure. A recent change to the colour of the cross on Nurse Bunnykins uniform from red to green may add a premium to figures with the original red colouring. Although if the current version is discontinued, it could be that the green cross variation will be rarer than the red.

It is almost unheard of for pilot versions of Bunnykins figures to 'escape' onto the market. Although recently there have been reports of the new Royal Doulton International Collectors Club fifteenth birthday Bunnykins figure making an unscheduled early appearance at an antiques fair. A more legitimate exception was the prototype of Uncle Sam Bunnykins which was auctioned for charity in the U.S.A. in 1992. This version was almost identical to the standard colouring except his bow tie was yellow rather than red. As only one copy is known in circulation it is interesting for the collector to know that the variation exists, but it does not really form part of the collection proper.

Beatrix Potter Figures

The story is somewhat different with regard to Beatrix Potter figures. At least nineteen figures have been remodelled or recoloured in some way. Some have been changed more than once. Some changes were for technical reasons, and some for practical reasons to make production easier. For example Mrs. Rabbit's umbrella was originally positioned away from her body and therefore vulnerable to being broken off. The figure was remodelled with the umbrella against her skirt. Some of the colour changes are the result of suggestions from the copyright holders of the original books to bring the figure more in line with the illustrations. Other colourings vary due to changes in ceramic paint formulas. On other occasions changes were made simply to make the figure more attractive.

Listed below are the nineteen figures which are known to exist in varying forms. There may be more. The publishers would be pleased to hear from collectors who have found other variations.

1105 Benjamin Bunny
1 Pale green jacket, light green beret with yellow and orange pom-poms. Ears out, shoes out.
2 Brown jacket, dark green beret with orange pom-pom. Ears out, shoes in
3 Tan jacket, green beret with orange pom-pom. Ears in, shoes in.
2803 Benjamin Bunny Sat on a Bank
1 Brown jacket. Head looks down.
2 Golden-brown jacket. Head looks up.
1941 Cecily Parsley
1 Blue dress, white apron, brown pail. Head down.
2 Blue dress, white apron, Head up.
2586 Fierce Bad Rabbit
1 Brown and white rabbit, red-brown carrot, green seat. Feet out.
2 Brown and white rabbit, red-brown carrot, green seat. Feet in.
1104 Little Pig Robinson
1 White and blue striped dress, brown basket with yellow cauliflowers.
2 Blue textured checked dress, brown basket with cream cauliflowers
1275 Miss Moppet
1 Dark brown mottled cat, blue checked kerchief.
2 Light brown striped cat, blue checked kerchief.
1940 Mr Benjamin Bunny
1 Dark maroon jacket, yellow waistcoat. Pipe out.
2 Lilac jacket, yellow waistcoat. Pipe in.
2453 Mr. Jackson
1 Green frog, mauve jacket

2 Brown frog, mauve jacket

1157 Mr. Jeremy Fisher
1 Green frog with small brown spots on head and legs. Lilac coat.
2 Green frog with large spots on head and stripes on legs. Lilac coat.
3 Green frog. Lilac coat.

1200 Mrs Rabbit
1 Pink and yellow striped dress, red collar and cap. Yellow straw coloured basket. Umbrella out.
2 Rose-pink and yellow striped dress, red collar and cap. Light straw coloured basket. Umbrella moulded to dress.
3 White, pink, yellow and green costume.

1107 Mrs. Tiggywinkle
1 Red-brown and white dress, green and blue striped skirt, white apron. The stripes are diagonal.
2 Red-brown and white dress, green and blue striped skirt, white apron. Square stripes.

1098 Peter Rabbit
1 Brown and white rabbit wearing medium blue jacket.
2 Brown and white rabbit wearing light blue jacket.

1365 Pigling Bland
1 Maroon jacket, blue waistcoat, yellow trousers.
2 Lilac jacket, blue waistcoat, yellow trousers.

2452 Sally Henny-Penny
1 Brown and gold chicken. Black hat and cloak, two yellow chicks. Mouth open.
2 Brown and gold chicken. Black hat and cloak, two yellow chicks. Mouth closed.

1102 Squirrel Nutkin
1 Red-brown squirrel holding green-brown nut.
2 Golden-brown squirrel holding green nut

1676 Tabitha Twitchit
1 Blue and white striped dress, white apron, blue striped top.
2 Blue and white striped dress, white apron, white top.

1101 Timmy Tiptoes
1 Grey squirrel with brown shading wearing red jacket.
2 Grey squirrel wearing pink jacket.

1100 Tom Kitten
1 Tabby kitten wearing medium blue trousers and jacket. Dark grren base.
2 Tabby kitten wearing darker blue trousers and jacket. Light green base.

1348 Tommy Brock
1 Blue jacket, pink waistcoat, yellow-green trousers. Small eye patch. Handle of spade out.
2 Blue jacket, red waistcoat, yellow-green trousers. Darker green base. Handle of spade out. Large eye patch.
3 Blue jacket, pink waistcoat, yellow-green trousers. Small eye patch. Handle of spade in.
4 Darker blue jacket, red waistcoat, yellow-green trousers. Large eye-patch. Handle of spade in.

Beatrix Potter Figure Backstamps

The backstamps used on Beatrix Potter figures have changed many times since 1948. Unlike Bunnykins figure backstamps they can be a useful aid in dating a particular piece as the figures did not retain their original mark but as backstamps changed all current production was marked with the new backstamp. Broadly speaking there are three styles of backstamp, Beswick Gold, Beswick brown and Royal Albert. However the backstamps are a little more complex than this. Illustrated below are the three main types together with descriptions of the variations.

Beswick Gold

1   Circular Beswick mark. Beatrix Potter in upper case type, character's name in italic script, c1948.

2   Oval Beswick mark. Beatrix Potter in upper case type. Character's name in italic script, sometimes within quotation marks. Can occur with 'copyright' in italic script, again c1948.

An example of Beswick Gold backstamp.

3   Oval Beswick mark. Beatrix Potter in upper case type. Character's name in upper case type within quotation marks.

4   Oval Beswick mark. Beatrix Potter and character's name in hand-written style script, c1955.

5   Oval Beswick mark. Beatrix Potter in upper case type, character's name in script. From 1961.

6   Oval Beswick mark. Beatrix Potter in upper case type, character's name in lower case type. Can occur with Beatrix Potter in slanted type. From 1971.

7   Oval Beswick mark. Beatrix Potter in upper case type, character's name in upper case type. 1971-72

Beswick Brown

1   Beswick England. F. Warne & Co. Ltd, Beatrix Potter and the character's name in upper case type. Character name in quotation marks. Copyright date included. 1972

An Example of Beswick Brown backstamp.

2   Beswick England. Beatrix Potter in upper case type. F. Warne & Co. Ltd and character's name in lower case type. Character's name in quotation marks. Copyright date included. 1974.

3   Beswick Made in England. Beatrix Potter in upper case type. F. Warne & Co. Ltd and character's name in lower case type. Character's name in quotation marks. Copyright date included.. 1973

4   Beswick England. Beatrix Potter in upper case type. F. Warne & Co. Ltd and character's name in lower case type. Copyright date included. 1974.

5   Beswick England. Beswick England. Beatrix Potter in upper case type. Frederick Warne PLC and character's name in lower case type. Character's name in quotation marks. Copyright date included.. 1982.

6   Beswick England. Beatrix Potter (no's) in upper case type. Character's name in lower case type with quotation marks. F. Warne & Co. in lower case. Licensed by Copyrights added. 1984.

7   Beswick England. Beatrix Potter (no's) in upper case type. Character's name in lower case type with quotation marks. Frederick Warne & Co in lower case. Licensed by Copyrights added. 1985

8   John Beswick script mark. Beatrix Potter in upper case type. Character's name in lower case type with quotation marks. F. Warne & Co. and licensed by Copyrights in lower case type. John Beswick in script. Studio of Royal Doulton in lower case type. 1988.

9   John Beswick script mark. Beatrix Potter in upper case type. Character's name in lower case type with quotation marks. Frederick Warne & Co. and licensed by Copyrights in lower case type. John Beswick in script. Studio of Royal Doulton in lower case type. 1988.

10 Commemorative mark.
   Used in 1993 on large size Peter Rabbit – centenary of Peter Rabbit.
   Used in 1994 on large size Jemima Puddle-Duck – centenary of Beswick
   factory.

Royal Albert
Gold Mark Royal Albert Crown mark in gold to
celebrate the brand name change in 1989. Also
occurs without the crown.

   Only used on six figures:
Peter Rabbit
Benjamin Bunny
Mrs Rabbit and Bunnies
Hunca Munca
Flopsy, Mopsy and Cottontail
Jemema Puddle-Duck

Brown Mark Royal Albert Crown mark. Also
occurs without the crown. 1989 to date.

*The Royal Albert backstamp
currrently in use of Beatrix
Potter figures.*

Gentleman Mouse Made a Bow P3200 and Ribby and the Patty Pan P3280.

Beatrix Potter Listings and Values

DB no	Version	Issued	Height	Backstamp	Market Value

Amiable Guinea Pig™ Modeller Albert Hallam   *picture page 42*

DB no	Version	Issued	Height	Backstamp	Market Value	
2061	1	1967-1983	3½"	Gold	£320-£330	$775-$825
2061	1	1967-1983	3½"	Brown	£220-£230	$490-$510

And This Pig Had None™ Modeller Martyn Alcock

3319	1	1992-Cur	4"	RA	£14	$30

Anna Maria™ Modeller Albert Hallam   *picture page 40*

1851	1	1963-1983	3"	Gold	£170-£180	$520-$530
1851	1	1963-1983	3"	Brown	£90-£110	$270-$280

Appley Dapply™ Modeller Albert Hallam   *picture page 46*

2333	1	1971-1980	3¼"	Gold	£90-£100	$220-$230
2333	2	1980-Cur	3¼"	Gold	£90-£100	$220-$230
2333	2	1980-Cur	3¼"	Brown	£40-£50	$70-$80
2333	2	1980-Cur	3¼"	RA	£14	$30

Aunt Pettitoes™ Modeller Albert Hallam   *picture page 48*

2276	1	1970-1993	3¾"	Gold	£90-£100	$320-$330
2276	1	1970-1993	3¾"	Brown	£40-£50	$70-$80
2276	1	1970-1993	3¾"	RA	£10-£20	$40-$50

Babbitty Bumble™ Modeller Warren Platt

2971	1	1989-1993	2¾"	RA	£20-£30	$50-$60

Benjamin Ate A Lettuce Leaf™ Modeller Martyn Alcock

3317	1	1992-Cur	4¾"	RA	£14	$30

DB no	Version	Issued	Height	Backstamp	Market Value	

Benjamin Bunny™ Modeller Arthur Gredington   *picture page 34, 35*

DB no	Version	Issued	Height	Backstamp	Market Value	
1105	1	1948-1974	4″	Gold	£250-£300	$575-$625
1105	2	1972-1980	4″	Gold	£250-£300	$475-$525
1105	3	1980-Cur	4″	Brown	£40-£50	$50-$70
1105	3	1980-Cur	4″	RA	£14	$30

Benjamin Bunny™ Modeller Martyn Alcock

1105	4	1994	6¼″	Beswick £27		$70

Benjamin Bunny Sat On A Bank™ Modeller David Lyttleton

2803	1	1983-1988	3¾″	Gold	£90-£100	$120-$130
2803	1	1983-1988	3¾″	Brown	£60-£70	$170-$180
2803	2	1988-Cur	3¾″	Brown	£45	$75
2803	2	1988-Cur	3¾″	RA	£14	$30

Benjamin Wakes Up™ Modeller Amanda Hughes-Lubeck

3234	1	1991-Cur	2¼″	RA	£14	$30

Cecily Parsley™ Modeller Arthur Gredington

1941	1	1965-1979	4″	Gold	£90-£100	$320-$330
1941	2	1979-1993	4″	Brown	£40-£50	$70-$80
1941	2	1979-1993	4″	RA	£20-£30	$25-$35

Chippy Hackee™ Modeller David Lyttleton   *picture page 45*

2627	1	1979-1993	3¾″	Brown	£40-£50	$80-$90
2627	1	1979-1993	3¾″	RA	£15-£25	$30-$50

Christmas Stocking™ Modeller Martyn Alcock

3257	1	1991-1994	3¼″	RA	£25-£35	$60-$70

Cottontail™ Modeller David Lyttleton   *picture page 47*

2878	1	1985-Cur	3¾″	Brown	£45	$60
2878	1	1985-Cur	3¾″	RA	£14	$30

DB no	Version	Issued	Height	Backstamp	Market Value	

Cousin Ribby™ Modeller Albert Hallam *picture page 47*

2284	1	1970-1993	3½"	Gold	£120-£130	$240-$260
2284	1	1970-1993	3½"	Brown	£40-£50	$60-$70
2284	1	1970-1993	3½"	RA	£15-£25	$25-$35

Diggory Diggory Delvet™ Modeller David Lyttleton *picture page 45*

| 2713 | 1 | 1982-Cur | 2¾" | Brown | £45 | $70 |
| 2713 | 1 | 1982-Cur | 2¾" | RA | £14 | $30 |

Display Stand™ Modeller Andrew Brindley

| 2295 | 1 | 1970-Cur | 12½" | Brown | £120-£130 | $140-$160 |
| 2295 | 1 | 1970-Cur | 12½" | Doulton | £40-£50 | $45-$55 |

Duchess™ Modeller Graham Orwell *picture page 38*

| 1355 | 1 | 1955-1967 | 3¾" | Gold | £2000-£2500 | $3500-$4000 |

Duchess™ Modeller Graham Tongue *picture page 40*

| 2601 | 2 | 1979-1982 | 4" | Brown | £220-£230 | $325-$350 |

Fierce Bad Rabbit™ Modeller David Lyttleton *picture page 46*

2586	1	1977-1980	4¾"	Brown	£140-£150	$220-$230
2586	2	1980-Cur	4¾"	Brown	£45	$70
2586	2	1980-Cur	4¾"	RA	£14	$30

Flopsy, Mopsy and Cottontail™ Modeller Arthur Gredington *p41*

1274	1	1954-Cur	2½"	Gold	£95	$350
1274	1	1954-Cur	2½"	Brown	£40	$70
1274	1	1954-Cur	2½"	RA	£14	$30

Foxy Reading Country News™ Modeller Amanda Hughes-Lubeck

| 3219 | 1 | 1990-Cur | 4¼" | RA | £22 | $55 |

Foxy Whiskered Gentleman™ Modeller Arthur Gredington *p41*

1277	1	1954-Cur	4¾"	Gold	£125	$300
1277	1	1954-Cur	4¾"	Brown	£55	$65
1277	1	1954-Cur	4¾"	RA	£14	$30

DB no	Version	Issued	Height	Backstamp	Market Value

Foxy Whiskered Gentleman™ Modeller Amanda Hughes-Lubeck

3450	1	1995-Cur	7"	RA	£27	$0

Gentleman Mouse Made A Bow™ Modeller Ted Chawner

3200	1	1990-Cur	3"	RA	£14	$30

Ginger™ Modeller David Lyttleton   *picture page 40*

2559	1	1976-1982	3¾"	Brown	£400-£425	$840-$860

Goody And Timmy Tiptoes™ Modeller David Lyttleton

2957	1	1986-Cur	4"	Brown	£165	$275
2957	1	1986-Cur	4"	RA	£25	$55

Goody Tiptoes™ Modeller Arthur Gredington

1675	1	1961-Cur	3½"	Gold	£95	$275
1675	1	1961-Cur	3½"	Brown	£45	$65
1675	1	1961-Cur	3½"	RA	£14	$30

Hunca Munca™ Modeller Arthur Gredington   *picture page 44*

1198	1	1951-Cur	2¾"	Gold	£125	$295
1198	1	1951-Cur	2¾"	Brown	£55	$100
1198	1	1951-Cur	2¾"	RA	£14	$30

Hunca Munca Spills The Beads™ Modeller Martyn Alcock

3288	1	1992-Cur	3¼"	RA	£16	$34

Hunca Munca Sweeping™ Modeller David Lyttleton   *picture page 48*

2584	1	1977-Cur	3½"	Brown	£65	$65
2584	1	1977-Cur	3½"	RA	£14	$30

Jemima Puddleduck™ Modeller Arthur Gredington *picture page 34, 48*

1092	1	1948-Cur	4¾"	Gold	£125	$275
1092	1	1948-Cur	4¾"	Brown	£45	$100
1092	1	1948-Cur	4¾"	RA	£14	$30
3373	2	1994	6"	RA	£25-£30	$60-$70

DB no	Version Issued		Height	Backstamp	Market Value

Jemima Puddleduck & Foxy Whiskered Gentleman™
Modeller Ted Chawner

3193	1	1990-Cur	4¾″	RA	£25	$80

Jemima Puddleduck & Foxy Whiskered Gentleman™
Modellers Harry Sales & David Lyttleton

2594	1	1977-1982	7½″	Brown	£70-£80	$170-$180

Jemima Puddleduck Character Jug™ Modeller Ted Chawner   *p39*

3088	1	1989-1992	4″	Brown	£70-£80	$140-$160
3088	1	1989-1992	4″	RA	£40-£50	$110-$120

Jemima Puddleduck Made A Feathered Nest™ Modeller David Lyttleton

2823	1	1983-Cur	2¼″	Brown	£35	$65
1823	1	1983-Cur	2¼″	RA	£14	$30

Jemima Puddleduck Wall Figural™ Modeller Albert Hallam   *p38*

2082	1	1967-1969	6″	Gold	£2000	$3500

John Joiner™ Modeller Graham Tongue

2965	1	1990-Cur	2½″	RA	£14	$30

Johnny Townmouse™ Modeller Arthur Gredington   *picture page 45*

1276	1	1954-1993	3½″	Gold	£120-£130	$270-$280
1276	1	1954-1993	3½″	Brown	£40-£50	$70-$80
1276	1	1954-1993	3½″	RA	£10-£20	$25-$35

Johnny Townmouse With Bag™ Modeller Ted Chawner   *p44*

1394	1	1988-1994	3½″	Gold	£190-£200	$240-$260
1394	1	1988-1994	3½″	Brown	£18	$50

Lady Mouse™ Modeller Arthur Gredington   *picture page 46*

1183	1	1950-Cur	4″	Gold	£125	$275
1183	1	1950-Cur	4″	Brown	£60	$85
1183	1	1950-Cur	4″	RA	£14	$30

DB no	Version	Issued	Height	Backstamp		Market Value

Lady Mouse Made A Curtsey™ Modeller Amanda Hughes-Lubeck

| 3220 | 1 | 1990-Cur | 3¼" | RA | £14 | $30 |

Little Black Rabbit™ Modeller David Lyttleton   *picture page 41*

| 2585 | 1 | 1977-Cur | 4½" | Brown | £45 | $75 |
| 2585 | 1 | 1977-Cur | 4½" | RA | £14 | $30 |

Little Pig Robinson™ Modeller Arthur Gredington   *picture page 44*

1104	1	1948-1970	4"	Gold	£190-£200	$490-$510
1104	2	1970-Cur	3½"	Brown	£45	$75
1104	2	1970-Cur	3½"	RA	£14	$30

Little Pig Robinson Spying™ Modeller Ted Chawner *picture page 44*

| 3031 | 1 | 1987-1993 | 3½" | Brown | £160-£170 | $270-$280 |
| 3031 | 1 | 1987-1993 | 3½" | RA | £30 | $100 |

Miss Dormouse™ Modeller Marty Alcock

| 3251 | 1 | 1991-1995 | 4" | RA | £20-£30 | $60-$70 |

Miss Moppet™ Modeller Arthur Gredington

1275	1	1954-c1978	3"	Gold	£120-£130	$235-$245
1275	2	1954-Cur	3"	Brown	£45	$75
1275	2	1954-Cur	3"	RA	£14	$30

Mittens And Moppet™ Modeller Ted Chawner

| 3197 | 1 | 1990-1994 | 3¾" | RA | £20-£30 | $40-$60 |

Mother Ladybird™ Modeller Warren Platt

| 2966 | 1 | 1989-Cur | 2½" | RA | £14 | $34 |

Mr Alderman Ptolemy™ Modeller Graham Tongue   *picture page 43*

| 2424 | 1 | 1973-Cur | 3½" | Brown | £95 | $95 |
| 2424 | 1 | 1973-Cur | 3½" | RA | £14 | $30 |

DB no	Version	Issued	Height	Backstamp	Market Value	

Mr Benjamin Bunny™ Modeller Arthur Gredington   *picture page 37*

1940	1	1965-1974	4¼"	Gold	£270-£280	$590-$610
1940	1	1965-1974	4¼"	Brown	£220-£230	$490-$510
1940	2	1974-Cur	4½"	Brown	£45	$75
1940	2	1974-Cur	4½"	RA	£14	$30

Mr Benjamin Bunny and Peter Rabbit™
Modeller Alan Maslankowski   *picture page 43*

| 2509 | 1 | 1975-1995 | 4" | Brown | £90-£100 | $220-$230 |
| 2509 | 1 | 1975-1995 | 4" | RA | £20-£30 | $45-$55 |

Mr Drake Puddleduck™ Modeller David Lyttleton   *picture page 47*

| 2628 | 1 | 1979-Cur | 4" | Brown | £50 | $75 |
| 2628 | 1 | 1979-Cur | 4" | RA | £14 | $30 |

Mr Jackson™ Modeller Albert Hallam   *picture page 43*

2453	1	1974-1980	2¾"	Brown	£220-£230	$445-$455
2453	2	1980-Cur	2¾"	Brown	£55	$75
2453	2	1980-Cur	2¾"	RA	£14	$30

Mr Jeremy Fisher™ Modeller Arthur Gredington   *picture page 34, 43*

1157	1	1950-1980	3"	Gold	£140-£150	$320-$330
1157	1	1950-1980	3"	Brown	£90-£100	$190-$210
1157	2	1980-Cur	3"	Brown	£45	$85
1157	2	1980-Cur	3"	RA	£14	$30

Mr Jeremy Fisher™ Modeller Martyn Alcock

| 3372 | 3 | 1994 | 5" | RA | £27 | $65 |

Mr Jeremy Fisher Character Jug™ Modeller Graham Tongue   *p39*

| 2960 | 4 | 1987-1992 | 3" | Brown | £60-£70 | $130-$140 |
| 2960 | 4 | 1987-1992 | 3" | RA | £40-£50 | $110-$120 |

Mr Jeremy Fisher Digging™ Modeller Ted Chawner   *p37, 46*

| 3090 | 1 | 1986-1994 | 3¾" | Brown | £170-£180 | $270-$280 |
| 3090 | 1 | 1986-1994 | 3¾" | RA | £20-£30 | $40-$60 |

DB no	Version	Issued	Height	Backstamp	Market Value	

Mr Tod™ Modeller Ted Chawner

DB no	Version	Issued	Height	Backstamp	Market Value	
3091	1	1988-1993	4¾″	Brown	£270-£280	$270-$280
3091	1	1988-1993	4¾″	RA	£25-£35	$90-$100

Mrs Flopsy Bunny™ Modeller Arthur Gredington   *picture page 47*

1942	1	1965-Cur	4″	Gold	£95	$225
1942	1	1965-Cur	4″	Brown	£45	$65
1942	1	1965-Cur	4″	RA	£14	$30

Mrs Rabbit™ Modeller Arthur Gredington   *picture page 34, 35, 36*

1200	1	1951-1970	4¼″	Gold	£220-£230	$395-$405
1200	1	1951-1970	4¼″	Brown	£140-£150	$245-$255
1200	2	1970-Cur	4¼″	Brown	£45	$75
1200	2	1970-Cur	4¼″	RA	£14	$30

Mrs Rabbit™ Modeller Martyn Alcock

1200	3	1994	6¼″	RA	£27	$65

Mrs Rabbit and Bunnies™ Modeller David Lyttleton

2543	1	1976-Cur	3¾″	Brown	£45	$95
2543	1	1976-Cur	3¾″	RA	£14	$30

Mrs Rabbit Cooking™ Modeller Martyn Alcock

3278	1	1992-Cur	4″	RA	£14	$30

Mrs Tiggywinkle™ Modeller Arthur Gredingon   *picture page 44*

1107	1	1948-1970	3¼″	Gold	£140-£150	$290-$310
1107	1	1948-1970	3¼″	Brown	£90-£100	$270-$280
1107	2	1970-Cur	3¼″	Brown	£45	$95
1107	2	1970-Cur	3¼″	RA	£14	$30

Mrs Tiggywinkle Character Jug™ Modeller Ted Chawner   *p39*

3102	1	1988-1992	3″	Brown	£60-£70	$140-$160
3102	1	1988-1992	3″	RA	£40-£50	$110-$120

DB no	Version	Issued	Height	Backstamp	Market Value	

Mrs Tiggywinkle Takes Tea™ Modeller David Lyttleton

| 2877 | 1 | 1985-Cur | 3¼″ | Brown | £95 | $95 |
| 2877 | 1 | 1985-Cur | 3¼″ | RA | £14 | $30 |

Mrs Tittlemouse™ Modeller Athur Gredington   *picture page 48*

1103	1	1948-1993	3½″	Gold	£120-£130	$290-$310
1103	1	1948-1993	3½″	Brown	£55-£65	$70-$80
1103	1	1948-1993	3½″	RA	£20-£30	$30-$40

Mrs Tittlemouse Plaque™ Modeller Harry Sales

| 2685 | 1 | 1982-1984 | 7½″ | Brown | £70-£80 | $145-$155 |

No More Twist™ Modeller Martyn Alcock

| 3325 | 1 | 1992-Cur | 7½″ | RA | £14 | $30 |

Old Mr Bouncer™ Modeller David Lyttleton   *picture page 48*

| 2956 | 1 | 1986-1995 | 3″ | Brown | £40-£50 | $70-$80 |
| 2956 | 1 | 1986-1995 | 3″ | RA | £15-£25 | $25-$30 |

Old Mr Brown™ Modeller Albert Hallam   *picture page 42, 46*

1796	1	1963-Cur	3″	Gold	£95	$200
1796	1	1963-Cur	3″	Brown	£45	$75
1796	1	1963-Cur	3″	RA	£14	$30

Old Mr Brown Character Jug™ Modeller Graham Tongue   *p39*

| 2959 | 1 | 1987-1992 | 3″ | Brown | £60-£70 | $145-$155 |
| 2959 | 1 | 1987-1992 | 3″ | RA | £40-£50 | $110-$120 |

Old Mr Pricklepin™ Modeller David Lyttleon   *picture page 36*

| 2767 | 1 | 1983-1989 | 2½″ | Brown | £70-£80 | $145-$155 |
| 2767 | 1 | 1983-1989 | 2½″ | RA | £30-£40 | $90-$110 |

Peter and the Red Pocket Handkerchief™
Modeller Martyn Alcock

| 3242 | 1 | 1991-Cur | 4¾″ | RA | £16 | $45 |

DB no	Version	Issued	Height	Backstamp	Market Value	

Peter in Bed™ Modeller Martyn Alcock

| 3473 | 1 | 1995-Cur | 2¾″ | RA | £19 | $0 |

Peter Rabbit™ Modeller Arthur Gredington   *picture page 34, 36*

1098	1	1948-1980	4½″	Gold	£140-£150	$270-$280
1091	1	1948-1980	4½″	Brown	£60-£70	$145-$155
1098	2	1980-Cur	4½″	Brown	£45	$65
1098	2	1980-Cur	4½″	RA	£14	$30
3356	3	1993	6¾″	Beswick	£30	$65

Peter Rabbit™ Modeller Martyn Alcock

| 3356 | 3 | 1993-Cur | 6¾″ | RA | £27 | $60 |

Peter Rabbit Character Jug™ Modeller Graham Tongue   *p39*

| 3006 | 1 | 1987-1992 | 3″ | Brown | £60-£70 | $145-$155 |
| 3006 | 1 | 1987-1992 | 3″ | RA | £40-£50 | $110-$120 |

Peter Rabbit in Gooseberry Net™ Modeller David Lyttleton

| 3157 | 1 | 1989-1995 | 2″ | RA | £15-£20 | $45-$55 |

Peter Rabbit Plaque™ Modeller Harry Sales & David Lyttleton

| 2650 | 2 | 1979-1983 | 7½″ | Brown | £60-£70 | $140-$150 |

Peter Rabbit Wall Figural™ Modeller Graham Tongue

| 2083 | 1 | 1967-1969 | 6″ | Gold | £2000 | $3500 |

Pickles™ Modeller Albert Hallam   *picture page 40*

| 2334 | 1 | 1971-1982 | 4½″ | Gold | £270-£280 | $740-$760 |
| 2334 | 1 | 1971-1982 | 4½″ | Brown | £220-£230 | $420-$430 |

Pig-Wig™ Modeller Albert Hallam

| 2381 | 1 | 1972-1982 | 4″ | Gold | £490-£510 | $590-$610 |
| 2381 | 1 | 1972-1982 | 4″ | Brown | £370-£380 | $775-$825 |

DB no	Version	Issued	Height	Backstamp	Market Value

Pigling Bland™ Modeller Graham Orwell   *picture page 35*

DB no	Version	Issued	Height	Backstamp	Market Value	
1365	1	1955-1970	4¼″	Gold	£270-£280	$590-$610
1365	2	1970-Cur	4¼″	Gold	£190	$295
1365	2	1970-Cur	4¼″	Brown	£45	$65
1365	2	1970-Cur	4¼″	RA	£14	$30

Pigling Eats His Porridge™ Modeller Martyn Alcock

3252	1	1991-1994	4″	RA	£15-£25	$45-$55
3252	1	1991-1994	4″	RA	£15-£25	$45-$55

Poorly Peter Rabbit™ Modeller David Lyttleton   *picture page 41*

2560	1	1976-Cur	3¾″	Brown	£45	$75
2560	1	1976-Cur	3¾″	RA	£14	$45

Rebeccah Puddleduck™ Modeller David Lyttleton   *picture page 36*

2647	1	1981-Cur	3¼″	Brown	£45	$75
2647	1	1981-Cur	3¼″	RA	£14	$30

Ribby™ Modeller Arthur Gredington   *picture page 36*

1199	1	1951-Cur	3¼″	Gold	£145	$225
1199	1	1951-Cur	3¼″	Brown	£45	$65
1199	1	1951-Cur	3¼″	RA	£14	$30

Ribby and the Patty Pan™ Modeller Martyn Alcock

3280	1	1992-Cur	3½″	RA	£14	$30

Sally Henny Penny™ Modeller Albert Hallam   *picture page 41*

2452	1	1974-1980	4″	Brown	£120-£130	$145-$155
2452	2	1980-1993	4″	Brown	£40-£50	$60-$70
2452	2	1980-1993	4″	RA	£20-£30	$40-$50

Samuel Whiskers™ Modeller Arthur Gredington   *picture page 44*

1106	1	1948-1995	3¾″	Gold	£140-£150	$290-$310
1106	1	1948-1995	3¾″	Brown	£40-£50	$70-$80
1106	1	1948-1995	3¾″	RA	£10-£20	$25-$35

DB no	Version	Issued	Height	Backstamp	Market Value	

Simpkin™ Modeller Alan Maslankowski — *picture page 40*

DB no	Version	Issued	Height	Backstamp	Market Value	
2508	1	1975-1983	4″	Brown	£400-£425	$875-$925

Sir Isaac Newton™ Modeller Graham Tongue — *picture page 37*

| 2425 | 1 | 1973-1984 | 3¾″ | Brown | £270-£280 | $490-$510 |

Squirrel Nutkin™ Modeller Arthur Gredington — *picture page 35*

1102	1	1948-1980	3¾″	Gold	£140-£150	$245-$255
1102	1	1948-1980	3¾″	Brown	£100-£120	$140-$160
1102	2	1980-Cur	3¾″	Brown	£45	$75
1102	2	1980-Cur	3¾″	RA	£14	$30

Susan™ Modeller David Lyttleton — *picture page 42*

| 2716 | 1 | 1983-1989 | 4″ | Brown | £120-£130 | $190-$210 |
| 2716 | 1 | 1983-1989 | 4″ | RA | £120-£130 | $140-$160 |

Tabitha Twitchit™ Modeller Arthur Greddington — *picture page 47*

1676	1	1961-1970	3½″	Gold	£130-£140	$270-$280
1676	1	1961-1970	3½″	Brown	£120-£130	$270-$280
1676	2	1970-1995	3½″	Gold	£140-£150	$240-$260
1676	2	1970-1995	3½″	Brown	£40-£50	$60-$70
1676	2	1970-1995	3½″	RA	£10-£20	$25-$35

Tabitha Twitchit and Miss Moppet™ Modeller David Lyttleton *p43*

| 2544 | 1 | 1976-1993 | 3½″ | Brown | £170-£180 | $190-$210 |
| 2544 | 1 | 1976-1993 | 3½″ | RA | £40-£50 | $70-$80 |

Tailor of Gloucester™ Modeller Arthur Gredington

1108	1	1949-Cur	3½″	Gold	£125	$250
1108	1	1949-Cur	3½″	Brown	£45	$65
1108	1	1949-Cur	3½″	RA	£14	$30

The Old Woman Who Lived In A Shoe™
Modeller Colin Melbourne — *picture page 48*

1545	1	1959-Cur	2¾″	Gold	£95	$225
1545	1	1959-Cur	2¾″	Brown	£45	$65
1545	1	1959-Cur	2¾″	RA	£14	$30

DB no	Version	Issued	Height	Backstamp	Market Value

The Old Woman Who Lived In A Shoe Knitting™
Modeller David Lyttleton   *picture page 47*

DB no	Version	Issued	Height	Backstamp	Market Value	
2804	1	1983-Cur	3″	Brown	£175	$250
2804	1	1983-Cur	3″	RA	£14	$30

The Tailor of Gloucester™ Modeller Warren Platt

3449	1	1995-Cur	7½″	RA	£27	$60

Thomasina Tittlemouse™ Modeller David Lyttleton   *picture page 36*

2668	1	1981-1990	3¼″	Brown	£70-£80	$120-$130
2668	1	1981-1990	3¼″	RA	£30-£40	$95-$105

Timmy Tiptoes™ Modeller Arthur Gredington   *picture page 45*

1101	1	1948-1980	3¾″	Gold	£120-£130	$240-$260
1101	1	1948-1980	3¾″	Brown	£105-£115	$140-$160
1101	2	1980-Cur	3½″	Brown	£45	$65
1101	2	1980-Cur	3½″	RA	£14	$30

Timmy Willie From Johnny Townmouse™
Modeller Arthur Gredington   *picture page 45*

1109	1	1949-1993	2½″	Gold	£120-£130	$240-$260
1109	1	1949-1993	2½″	Brown	£40-£50	$70-$80
1109	1	1949-1993	2½″	RA	£15-£25	$40-$50

Timmy Willie Sleeping™ Modeller Graham Tongue   *picture page 45*

2996	1	1986-Cur	1¼″	Brown	£175	$300
2996	1	1986-Cur	1¼″	RA	£14	$30

Tom Kitten™ Modeller Arthur Gredington   *picture page 34, 35, 41*

1100	1	1948-1980	3½″	Gold	£120-£130	$270-$280
1100	1	1948-1980	3½″	Brown	£105-£115	$220-$230
1100	2	1980-Cur	3½″	Brown	£45	$65
1100	2	1980-Cur	3½″	RA	£14	$30

Tom Kitten™ Modeller Martyn Alcock

3405	3	1994	5¼″	RA	£27	$65

DB no	Version	Issued	Height	Backstamp	Market Value	

Tom Kitten Character Jug™ Modeller Ted Chawner *picture page 39*

| 3103 | 1 | 1989-1992 | 3″ | Brown | £60-£70 | $145-$155 |
| 3103 | 1 | 1989-1992 | 3″ | RA | £40-£50 | $110-$120 |

Tom Kitten Plaque™ Modeller Graham Tongue *picture page 38*

| 2085 | 1 | 1967-1969 | 6″ | Gold | £2000 | $3500 |

Tom Kitten and Butterfly™ Modeller Ted Chawner *picture page 43*

| 3030 | 1 | 1987-1994 | 3½″ | Brown | £170-£180 | $220-$230 |
| 3030 | 1 | 1987-1994 | 3½″ | RA | £15-£25 | $40-$60 |

Tom Thumb™ Modeller Warren Platt *picture page 46*

| 2989 | 1 | 1987-Cur | 3¼″ | Brown | £95 | $165 |
| 2989 | 1 | 1987-Cur | 3¼″ | RA | £14 | $30 |

Tommy Brock™ Modeller Graham Orwell *picture page 35*

1348	1	1955-1970	3½″	Gold	£240-£250	$620-$630
1348	1	1955-1970	3½″	Gold	£220-£230	$520-$530
1348	4	1980-Cur	3½″	Brown	£45	$65
1348	4	1980-Cur	3½″	RA	£14	$30

Tree Lamp Base™ Modeller James Hayward & Albert Hallam

| 1531 | 1 | 1958-1982 | 7″ | Gold | £190-£210 | $270-$280 |
| 1531 | 1 | 1958-1982 | 7″ | Brown | £170-£180 | $220-$230 |

Beatrix Potter Colour Guide

Back row; left to right: P1105 Royal Albert Benjamin Bunny; P1092 Royal Albert Jemima Puddleduck; P1098 Royal Albert Peter Rabbit. Front row; left to right: P1100 Royal Albert Tom Kitten; P1157 Royal Albert Jeremy Fisher; P1200 Royal Albert Mrs Rabbit.

Back row; left to right: P1102 Squirrel Nutkin; P1105 Benjamin Bunny; P1348 Tommy Brock, all three being first version models.
Front row; left to right: P1200 Mrs Rabbit; P1365 Pigling Bland, 1st version; P1100 Tom Kitten.

*Back row; left to right: P2647 Rebeccah Puddleduck; P1098 Peter Rabbit; P1199 Ribby.
Front row; left to right: P1200 Mrs Rabbit; P2767 Old Mr Pricklepin; P2668 Thomasina
Tittlemouse.*

Back row; left to right: P1940 Mr Benjamin Bunny, 1st version; and two versions of P3090 Mr Jeremy Fisher Digging
Front row; left to right: P1940 Mr Benjamin Bunny, 2nd version; two versions of P2425 Sir Isaac Newton.

Left to right: P2085 Tom Kitten Wall Plaque; P1355 Duchess; P2082 Jemima Puddleduck Wall Plaque.

Back row; left to right: P2959 Old Mr Brown Character Jug; P2960 Jeremy Fisher Character Jug; P3088 Jemima Puddleduck Character Jug.
Front row; left to right: P3103 Tom Kitten Character Jug; P3102 Mrs Tiggywinkle Character Jug; P3006 Peter Rabbit Character Jug.

Back row; left to right: P2508 Simpkin; P2061 Amiable Guinea Pig; P2334 Pickles.
Front row; left to right: P1851 Anna Maria; P2601 Duchess; P2559 Ginger.

Back row; left to right: P2560 Poorly Peter Rabbit; P1277 Foxy Whiskered Gentleman; P2452 Sally Henny Penny.
Front row; left to right: P2585 Little Black Rabbit; P1274 Flopsy, Mopsy and Cottontail; P1100 Tom Kitten.

*Back row; left to right: P1796 Old Mr Brown; two versions of P2061 Amiable Guinea Pig.
Front row; left to right: P1796 Old Mr Brown; two examples of P2716 Susan.*

Back row; left to right: P2544 Tabitha Twitchit and Miss Moppet; P2424 Mr Alderman Ptolemy; P2509 Mr Benjamin Bunny and Peter Rabbit.
Front row; left to right: P1157 Jeremy Fisher; P3030 Tom Kitten and Butterfly; P2453 Mr Jackson.

Back row; left to right: P1106 Samuel Whiskers; P3031 Little Pig Robinson Spying; P1104 Little Pig Robinson.
Front row; left to right: P1107 Mrs Tiggywinkle; P1198 Hunca Munca; P1394 Johnny Townmouse with Bag.

Back row; left to right: P1276 Johhny Townmouse; P1101 Timmy Tiptoes; P2627 Chippy Hackee.
Front row; left to right: P1109 Timmy Willie; P2996 Timmy Willie Sleeping; P2713 Diggory Diggory Delvet.

Back row; left to right: P2586 Fierce Bad Rabbit; P1796 Old Mr Brown; P2333 Appley Dapply.
Front row; left to right: P3090 Mr Jeremy Fisher Digging; P1183 Lady Mouse; P2989 Tom Thumb.

Back row; left to right: P2878 Cottontail; P2628 Mr Drake Puddleduck; P1942 Mrs Flopsy Bunny.
Front row; left to right: P1676 Tabitha Twitchit; P2804 The Old Woman Who Lived In A Shoe Knitting; P2284 Cousin Ribby.

Back row; left to right: P2956 Old Mr Bouncer; P1092 Jemima Puddleduck; P2276 Aunt Pettitoes.
Front row; left to right: P2584 Hunca Munca Sweeping; P1545 The Old Woman Who Lived In a Shoe; P1103 Mrs Tittlemouse.

The Bunnykins Figure Story

It might be seen as improbable that the creator of Bunnykins was a nun. However, Barbara Vernon Bailey was a nun with connections. Her father was Cuthbert Bailey, the general manager of Royal Doulton's factory in Burslem, Stoke on Trent. It was he who saw the potential in the sketches of the rabbit family Sister Mary Barbara reguarly sent home from the convent school where she taught. The rabbits bore a strong likeness to her own family, in particular Father Rabbit with his round spectacles and ever present pipe which reminded many of Cuthbert Bailey himself. He obviously did not mind the comparison as he had Barbara's drawings adapted for production on a range of Royal Doulton childrens china. The artist chosen to do this work was Hubert Light. Previously he had designed some of the early figures in Royal Doulton's HN range. His most enduring legacy to the Bunnykins collection is the familiar border of running rabbits which, albeit in a redrawn form, is still in use today. The new Bunnykins nurseyware was introduced in 1934 and at once proved successful. Gradually all other Royal Doulton nurseryware designs were withdrawn from production leaving Bunnykins to reign supreme. It consisted entirely of practical tableware pieces and apart from one or two additional items and various shape and body updates remains much the same.

The first decorative items were launched in 1939. These were the first Bunnykins figures, and were a family of rabbits, Farmer Bunnykin, Mother Bunnykin, and their four 'children', Billy, Reggie, Mary and Freddie. Royal Doulton promoted them, together with a bunny-shaped range of tableware, as part of the Bunnykins range. However the models have little in common with the Bunnykins family as portrayed on the nurseyware. These early figures, which are thought to have been designed by Royal Doulton's Art Director, Charles Noke, are more akin to some of the anthropomorphic figures in the HN range. Nevertheless they have always been considered as part of the Bunnykins collection and carried the Bunnykins backstamp. Interestingly they are usually marked Bunnykin rather than Bunnykins. The production life of these figures was remarkably short as the outbreak of the 2nd World War ended the production of most decorative ceramic items. When production slowly resumed after 1945 some pre-war items were reintroduced including Bunnykins nurseryware but not the Bunnykins figures

The popularity of Bunnykins tableware continued to increase in the post-war years. Walter Hayward, who for some time had adpted Barbara Vernon's sketches for production took over as designer. Barbara Vernon's facsimile signature continued to be used for a while but Hayward's style was rather different and recognisable. The scenes have more rabbits in them and little mice take a more active part in the proceedings.

Bunnykins Figures Make a Comeback

It was not until the early 1970's that the idea of a range of complimentary Bunnykins figures was again considered. The acquisition of the Beswick factory by Royal Doulton in 1969 may have influenced the decision to relaunch Bunnykins figures. The factory specialised in animal models and for twenty years or so had enjoyed great success with their Beatrix Potter figures. It was from this pool of experience that the new Bunnykins figures emerged. Indeed the style and scale of the new range had much more in common with the Beswick figures than the original Bunnykins figures of 1939. In fact the designer of the first Beatrix Potter figures, Albert Hallam, was also the creator of the new Bunnykins figures.

With the wealth of ideas available from the tablerware designs of Barbara Vernon and Walter Hayward it is not surprising that the first characters were directly lifted from nurseryware scenes. Between 1972 and 1974 fifteen models were introduced, all of them being taken directly from tableware designs. It is noticeable that the colour schemes used for the figures reflect the colourings of the original drawings.

After this initial burst of activity Royal Doulton seemed to loose interest in Bunnykins figures. No further figures were introduced for eight years but interestingly no figures were withdrawn either. This rather indicates that the company considered Bunnykins figures enough of a commercial success to remain in production but perhaps not quite successful enough to warrant too much promotional activity.

Bunnykins Figures Make a Comeback – Again

The renaissance of Bunnykins figures started for a second time in the early 1980's. Harry Sales had been appointed Design Manager of the Beswick factory in 1975. He was a great supporter of Bunnykins but saw that the potential for Bunnykins figures lay in a totally different direction to what had gone before. This is evident from the models which were introduced under his influence. The first of these introductions were a mixture of convential style characters such as **Mr. Bunnykins at the Easter Parade** (DB18) and **Santa Bunnykins** (DB17) and the new approach which is illustrated by **Jogging Bunnykins** (DB22) and the sporting Bunnykins which followed

The new style figures pass a witty comment on human activities and frailities. The expression on the face of **Jogging Bunnykins** strikes a cord with anyone who has seen an overweight jogger of the human variety valiantly plodding along the road, and the supreme optimism of **Bogey Bunnykins** looking in vain for his golf ball which remains steadfastly at his feet can be seen on any golf course at any time. The new style characters represent a move to broaden the appeal of the figures from being purely aimed at children into the adult collectables market. The entire family could now enjoy collecting Bunnykins figures.The new figures were obviously not so closely tied to the nurseryware range and employed a brighter selection of colours to add extra appeal to their intended audience.

Customised Bunnykins Figures

The 50th anniversary of Bunnykins was celebrated in 1984. The **Bunnykins Oompah Band** was issued in that year and as part of the promotional activity **Drummer Bunnykins** (DB26) carried on his drum the legend '50th Anniversary'. After 1984 the drum is inscribed 'Bunnykins Oompah Band'. 1984 was also an Olympic year. The games were held in Australia and a colourway of **Olympic Bunnykins** in the Australian national colours of green and gold was produced for the Australian market. The two events were the first instances of Bunnykins figures being customised. There followed two colourways for special events in the United States and **Uncle Sam Bunnykins** (DB50) was produced for sale in the U.S.A. **Collector Bunnykins** (DB54) was commissioned in 1987 by the Royal Doulton International Collectors Club. It had been the practice of the club to commission special pieces from the various Royal Doulton ranges exclusively for their members. At this point in the club's history the items were only available for a limited period of time, usually about six months. Two of the most popular items had been 'Prized Possessions' and 'Pride and Joy', a pair of seated figures showing somewhat elderly collectors studying the relevent reference books on their collecting interest, Royal Doulton Figures and Royal Doulton Character Jugs respectively. As the Bunnykins Collectors Book had recently been published it was appropriate that **Collector Bunnykins** should be shown in a similar pose. As this figure was only available for a very short time it is now considered one of the most difficult to find and consequently one of the most valuable. It is important as it played a vital part in awakening collectors interest in Bunnykins figures. It was also one of Harry Sales last Bunnykins designs as he left Royal Doulton in 1986.

Another Change of Direction

The next few years saw the increase in both withdrawals from production and the number of special commissions for Bunnykins figures. Bunnykins figure collecting started to come of age.

With the departure of Harry Sales the style of Bunnykins figures once again changed. Graham Tongue took over as Design Manager and consequently responsibility for the Bunnykins range. Under his guidance the subjects portayed moved away from adult activities to which which were intended to have appeal to younger children while having a slight educational aspect to them. Others featured childrens activities such as scouting – **Be Prepared Bunnykins** (DB56), and guides – **Brownie Bunnykins** (DB61). It is also noticeable that the rabbits themselves undergo a slight change, the poses become more 'human'.

The Influence of Colin Twinn's Designs

Changes were also happening to the designs used on Bunnykins tableware and these were to have an influence on the figures. In 1987 it was decided to publish a series of childrens books using the Bunnykins characters. There had been other Bunnykins publications but on this occasion the publisher was to be Frederick Warne and Co. Ltd. who were best known as the publisher and copyright holder of the Beatrix Potter stories. Colin Twinn, a successful childrens book illustrator was brought in to develop the Bunnykins characters for publication. It was intended to use some of his designs on the nurseryware. The result of Mr. Twinns work was a completely new look for Bunnykins. A new Bunnykins family was created who lived in a softer coloured world of idealised rolling countryside. The rabbits again metamorphosed with larger ears and slightly stylised bodies. A great number of scenes were eventually issued on the tableware to a mixed reception from the public. Some of Colin Twinns designs are still in production but the majority were withdrawn after a few years. However the Bunnykins figure collection gained a number of new characters. Some of the older subjects were remodelled and renamed to fit in with Colin Twinn's new Bunnykins family, for example **Family Photograph** (DB1) became **Father, Mother** and **Victoria Bunnykins** (DB68), **Tally Ho** (DB12) became **William Bunnykins** (DB69) and **Busy Needles** (DB10) became **Susan Bunnykins** (DB70). New members of the family were designed by Graham Tongue based on Colin Twinn's illustrations, (**Polly Bunnykins** DB71, **Tom Bunnykins** DB72 and **Harry Bunnykins** DB73). In general most of the introductions of the late 1980's show the influence of Colin Twinn's redesigned Bunnykins illustrations.

Bunnykins Figures in the 1990's

The market for Bunnykins figures in the 1990's has been dominated by special commissions. The ground breaking **Bunnykins Collectors Band** (DB86-90) led the way for many similar limited editions. In Great Britain U.K. International Ceramics consolidated their position as the prime source of new Bunnykins commissions. In other markets there has been a mixture of private commissions, such as Magician Bunnykins (DB126) and commissions originating from Royal Doulton's overseas companies, notably Royal Doulton Australia with **Aussie Surfer Bunnykins** (DB133) and Royal Doulton U.S.A. who have issued several colourways for promotional tours. The market for these special editions shows no sign of slowing down. Each new issue is greeted with enthusiasm by collectors, many of whom go to great lengths to obtain models not available in their home market.

Fifteen figures were withdrawn from production in 1993. Currently the collection consists of around twenty figures. At present it seems there will be more new models issued as special commissions than directly from Royal Doulton but this could easily change. What does not seem set for change however is the strength of the collectors market for Bunnykins figures.

The Bunnykins family are now set to become film stars. An animated film has been produced and sold to television stations around the world. It will eventually be made available to collectors in video form. The first public showing in Britiain will be at the UK Doulton Collectors Fair in October 1995.

The current popularity of Bunnykins figures is shown by the fact that the Royal Doulton International Collectors Club in the USA plans to issue a special double Bunnykins figure to celebrate the club's fifteenth birthday.

It would seem that it is not only **Surfer Bunnykins** who is riding the crest of the wave – the Bunnykins story just goes from strength to strength.

Bunnykins Backstamps

The backstamps used on Royal Doulton Bunnykins figures have been modified several times since 1972. This is a result of changes in Royal Doultons exact trading title. However as it would seem that once a Bunnykins figure is issued it retains the backstamp current at the time of issue for its entire production life backstamps are of very little help in dating the figure. By identifying the backstamp it is possible to ascertain, within a few years, the introduction date of the character. The date found incorporated in the backstamp is the date the figure was copyrighted, not necessarily the date of introduction. Usually the copyright is obtained the year before a model is added to the range. This however is not a hard and fast rule as there are some instances where a figure has been copyrighted and issued within the same year.

A feature of the Bunnykins market are the numerous special commissions and limited edition colurways. This has led to a number of backstamp variations which give details of the commissioning organisation and can also include some extra information. For example, Collector Bunnykins has a backstamp which not only records its exclusivity to members of the Royal Doulton International Collectors Club but also gives the modellers name, an unusual departure for a Bunnykins backstamp. The first backstamp which defines the size of a limited edition is to be found on Drummer Bunnykins (DB89), part of the Bunnykins Collectors Band. Although the Collectors Band consists of five figures it is only the Drummer who has this amended backstamp. It is now usual for the edition size to be recorded where it is appropriate.

The first, and so far only, individually numbered backstamp is to be found on Rock and Roll Bunnykins (DB124) which was commissioned by Royal Doulton U.S.A. in a limited edition of 1000 to celebrate the opening of the Cleveland Rock and Roll Hall of Fame in 1991.

Unlike Beatrix Potter figures the value of a Bunnykins figure is not affected by its backstamp.

Illustrated are six representative Bunnykins Figure backstamps.

Listed are descriptions of the various backstamps found on Bunnykins figures that have been on general sale.

1 Royal Doulton Lion and Crown backstamp. Bunnykins in upper case type. Character or title in lower case with quotation marks. Royal Doulton Tableware Ltd. in upper case type. Copyright date and DB number included. 1972-84.

Backstamp used on the first Bunnykins figures issued in 1939. Note the use of Bunnykin in the singular.

Backstamp used on Bunnykins figures c1974.

Backstamp currently in use on all Bunnykins figures on general sale.

The first, and so far only, individually numbered limited edition backstamp. Used for Rock and Roll Bunnykins.

There are two variations of this mark

a Royal Doulton Tableware Ltd changed to Doulton and Co. Limited, and design registration numbers included. c1974.

b For the 50th anniversary year of Bunnykins 'Golden Jubilee Celebrations' was added to the usual backstamp. Upper case type used. 1984.

2 Royal Doulton Lion and Crown backstamp. Character name or title in upper case type with quotation marks. Company name changed to Royal Dolton (UK). 1985-86.

3 Royal Doulton Lion and Crown backstamp. Title or character name in upper case type. (UK) dropped from company name. Used on all new models from 1977.

Special commissions and editions have an adapted Bunnykins backstamp and are self explanatory.

Backstamp used on Bunnykins figures commissioned by UK International Ceramics Ltd.

Backstamp used on Collector Bunnykins which was commissioned by the Royal Doulton International Collectors Club for sale only to its members.

Bunnykins Colour Guide

Back row; left to right: DB5 Autumn Days "Mr Bunnykins"; DB54 The Collector Bunnykins; DB58 Australian Bunnykins. Front row; left to right: DB11 Rise and Shine; DB20 Astro Bunnykins; DB58 Australian Colourway.

Back row; left to right: DB41 Freefall Bunnykins; DB1 Family Photograph; DB16 Mr Bunnybeat Strumming.
Front row; left to right: DB42 Ace Bunnykins; DB65 Lollipop Man Bunnykins.

Back row; left to right: DB76 Postman Bunnykins; DB18 Mr Bunnykins at the Easter Parade; DB80 Dollie Bunnykins Playtime.
Front row; left to right: DB77 Paperboy Bunnykins; DB43 Home Run Bunnykins; DB70 Susan Bunnykins.

Back row; left to right: DB10 Busy Needles; DB29 Touchdown Bunnykins; DB6 Mrs Bunnykins Clean Sweep.
Front row; left to right: DB22 Jogging Bunnykins; DB40 Aerobic Bunnykins; DB28 Olympic Bunnykins.

Back row; left to right: DB8 Dollie Bunnykins Playtime; DB126 Magician Bunnykins; DB84 Fisherman Bunnykins.
Front row; left to right: DB59 Storytime; DB69 William Bunnykins; DB31 Downhill Bunnykins.

*Back row; left to right: DB82 Ice Cream Bunnykins; DB124 Rock and Roll Bunnykins;
DB71 Polly Bunnykins.*
*Front row; left to right: DB61 Brownie Bunnykins; DB15 Sleepytime; DB72 Tom
Bunnykins.*

Back row; left to right: DB51 Mr Bunnykins at the Easter Parade; DB52 Mrs Bunnykins at the Easter Parade; DB67 Family Photograph.
Front row; left to right: DB103 Bedtime Bunnykins; DB63 Bedtime Bunnykins; DB81 Billie and Buntie Bunnykins Sleigh Ride

Back row; left to right: DB106 Trumpeter Bunnykins; DB108 Drummer Bunnykins; DB105 Sousaphone Bunnykins.
Front row; left to right: 109 Drum-Major Bunnykins; DB107 Cymbals Bunnykins.

Back row; left to right: DB73 Harry Bunnykins; DB83 Susan Bunnykins as Queen of the May; DB32 Bogey Bunnykins.
Front row; left to right: DB115 Harry the Herald; DB2 Buntie Bunnykins Helping Mother; DB98 Touchdown Bunnykins Cincinnati Bengals.

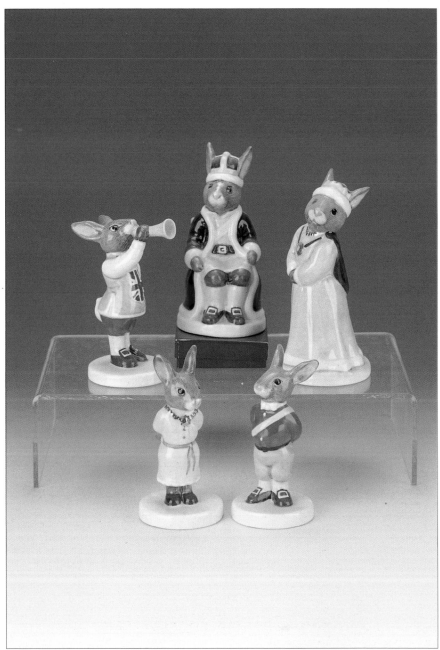

Back row; left to right: DB95 Harry the Herald; DB91 King John; DB92 Queen Sophie.
Front row; left to right: DB93 Princess Beatrice; DB94 Prince Frederick.

Back row; left to right: DB128 Clown Bunnykins; DB104 Carol Singer Bunnykins; DB129 Clown Bunnykins.
Front row; left to right: DB135 Constable Mountie Bunnykins; DB134 John Bull Bunnykins; DB127 Guardsman Bunnykins.

Back row; left to right: DB145 Bowler Bunnykins; DB144 Batsman Bunnykins;
DB150 Wicket Keeper Bunnykins.
Front row; left to right: DB125 Milkman Bunnykins; DB143 Cheerleader Bunnykins;
DB123 Soccer Player Bunnykins.

Back row; from left: 6004 Mother Bunnykins; 6025 Reggie Bunnykins; 6003 Farmer Bunnykins.
Front row; from left:6002 Mary Bunnykins; 6001 Billie Bunnykins; 6024 Freddie Bunnykins.

Bunnykins Listings and Values

DB No	Version	Production Dates	Height	Market value	

Ace Bunnykins™ Designer Harry Sales *picture page 58*

42	1	1986-1989	3¾"	£120-£130	$200-$220

Aerobic Bunnykins™ Designer Harry Sales *picture page 60*

40	1	1985-1988	2¾"	£70-£80	$120-$135

Astro Bunnykins Rocket Man™ Designer Harry Sales *picture page 57*

20	1	1983-1988	4¼"	£70-£80	$120-$135
35	1	1984-1989	7"	£70-£80	$120-$130

Aussie Surfer Bunnykins™ Designer Graham Tongue

133	1	1994	4"	£60-£70	$100-$120

Australian Bunnykins™ Designer Harry Sales *picture page 57*

58	1	1988	4"	£340-£360	$575-$610

Ballet Bunnykins™ Designer Unknown

44	1	Not put into production	N/A	N/A	

Bathtime Bunnykins™ Designer Graham Tongue

148	1	1994-cur	4"	£15	$40

Batsman Bunnykins™ Designer Denise Andrews *picture page 68*
Limited edition of 1000

144	1	1994	4"	£65-£80	$70-$80

Be Prepared Bunnykins™ Designer Graham Tongue

56	1	1987-cur	4"	£14	$40

DB No	Version	Production Dates	Height	Market value	

Bedtime Bunnykins™ Designer Graham Tongue   *picture page 63*

55	1	1987-cur	3¼″	£14	$40
63	2	1987	3¼″	£140-£160	$240-$270
79	3	1988	3¼″	£440-£460	$750-$780
103	4	1991	3¼″	£90-£100	$150-$170

Billie & Buntie Bunnykins Sleigh Ride™
Designer Walter Hayward   *picture page 63*

| 4 | 1 | 1972-cur | 3¼″ | £14 | $40 |
| 81 | 2 | 1989 | 3½″ | £70-£80 | $120-$140 |

Billie Bunnykins Cooling Off™ Designer Walter Hayward

| 3 | 1 | 1972-1987 | 3¾″ | £190-£200 | $320-$340 |

Billy Bunnykins™ Designer Charles Noke   *picture page 69*

| 6001 | 1 | 1939-c1940 | 4½″ | £800-£1200 | $1360-$2000 |

Bogey Bunnykins™ Designer Harry Sales   *picture page 65*

| 32 | 1 | 1985-1992 | 4″ | £60-£70 | $100-$120 |

Bowler Bunnykins™ Designer Denise Andrews   *picture page 68*
Limited edition of 1000

| 145 | 1 | 1994 | 4″ | £60-£80 | |

Boy Skater Bunnykins™ Designer Martyn Alcock

| 152 | 1 | 1995-cur | 3½″ | £17 | $40 |

Bride Bunnykins™ Designer Graham Tongue

| 101 | 1 | 1991-cur | 4″ | £17 | $40 |

Brownie Bunnykins™ Designer Graham Tongue   *picture page 62*

| 61 | 1 | 1987-1993 | 4″ | £25-£35 | $45-$55 |

Bunny Bank™ Designer Unknown

| 6615 | 1 | 1967-1977 | 8½″ | £180-£200 | $290-$310 |
| 6615 | 1 | 1979-1991 | 9¼″ | £140-£160 | $200-$220 |

DB No	Version	Production Dates	Height	Market value	

Buntie Bunnykins Helping Mother™ Designer Walter Hayward *p65*

2	1	1972-1993	3½″	£30-£40	$50-$70

Busy Needles Bunnykins™ Designer Walter Hayward

10	1	1973-1988	3¼″	£70-£80	$120-$140

Carol Singer Music Box™ Designer Harry Sales

53	1	1986-1989	7″	£90-£100	$150-$170

Carol Singer Bunnykins™ Designer Harry Sales   *picture page 67*
Limited edition of 1000

104	1	1991	4″	£70-£80	$120-$140

Cheerleader Bunnykins™ Designer Denise Andrews   *picture page 68*
Limited edition of 1000

142	1	1994	4½″	£40-£50	$70-$85
143	1	1994	4½″	£40-£50	$70-$85

Christmas Surprise Bunnykins™ Designer Graham Tongue

146	1	1994-1995	3½″	£15	$40

City Gent Teapot™ Designer Unknown

6966	1	1994	8″	£50	$95

Clown Bunnykins™ Designer Denise Andrews   *picture page 67*
Limited edition of 250 and 750

128	1	1992	4¼″	£350-£380	$590-$600
129	2	1992	4¼″	£600-£650	$1100-$1120

Collector Bunnykins™ Designer Harry Sales   *picture page 57*

54	1	1987	4¼″	£550-£600	$970-$990

Constable Mountie Bunnykins™ Designer Graham Tongue
Limited edition of 750   *picture page 67*

135	1	1993	4″	£145-£155	$250-$265

DB No	Version	Production Dates	Height	Market value	

Cook Bunnykins™ Designer Graham Tongue

| 85 | 1 | 1990-1994 | 4¼" | £10-£20 | $30-$40 |

Cymbals Bunnykins™ Designer Harry Sales *picture page 62*

25	1	1984-1990	3½"	£30-£40	$50-$70
88	1	1990	3½"	£90-£150	$185-$130
107	1	1991	4"	£120-£200	$220-$130

Daisie Bunnykins Springtime™ Designer Walter Hayward

| 7 | 1 | 1972-1983 | 3½" | £350-£380 | $650-$680 |

Dollie Bunnykins Playtime™ Designer Walter Hayward *p59, p61*

| 8 | 1 | 1972-1993 | 4" | £30-£40 | $50-$70 |
| 80 | 2 | 1988 | 4" | £50-£60 | $85-$100 |

Downhill Bunnykins™ Designer Harry Sales *picture page 61*

| 31 | 1 | 1985-1988 | 2½" | £90-£100 | $150-$170 |

Drum-Major Bunnykins™ Designer Harry Sales *picture page 62*

27	1	1984-1990	3½"	£30-£40	$50-$70
90	2	1990	3¾"	£90-£110	$150-$190
109	1	1991	3½"	£120-£130	$200-$220

Drummer Bunnykins™ Designer Harry Sales *picture page 64*

26	1	1984-1990	3½"	£90-£100	$150-$190
26	2	1984-1990	3¾"	£30-£40	$50-$70
89	3	1990	3¾"	£90-£110	$150-$185
108	1	1991	3½"	£120-£130	$200-$220

Easter Greetings Bunnykins™ Designer Graham Tongue

| 149 | 1 | 1995-cur | 3½" | £15 | $40 |

Family Photograph Bunnykins™ Designer Walter Hayward *p58, p63*

| 1 | 1 | 1972-1988 | 4½" | £80-£100 | |
| 67 | 2 | 1988 | 4½" | £70-£80 | $120-$140 |

DB No	Version	Production Dates	Height	Market value	

Farmer Bunnykins™ Designer Charles Noke   *picture page 69*

| 6003 | 1 | 1939-c1940s | 7½" | £1200-£1500 | $2050-$2550 |

Father, Mother and Victoria Bunnykins™
Designer Walter Hayward

| 68 | 1 | 1988-cur | 4½" | £16 | $40 |

Footballer Bunnykins™ Designer Denise Andrews
Limited edition of 250

117	1	1991	4½"	£85-£95	$145-$160
119	2	1991	4½"	£85-£95	$145-$160
121	3	1991	4½"	£85-£95	$145-$160

Fireman Bunnykins™ Designer Graham Tongue

| 75 | 1 | 1989 | 4¼" | £40-£50 | $70-$85 |

Fisherman Bunnykins™ Designer Graham Tongue   *picture page 61*

| 84 | 1 | 1990-1993 | 4¼" | £40-£50 | $70-$85 |

Freddie Bunnykins™ Designer Charles Noke   *picture page 69*

| 6024 | 1 | 1939-c1940s | 3¾" | £1500-£1800 | $2500-$3060 |

Freefall Bunnykins™ Designer Harry Sales   *picture page 58*

| 41 | 1 | 1986-1989 | 3¾" | £140-£160 | $200-$220 |

Girl Skater Bunnykins™ Designer Martyn Alcock

| 153 | 1 | 1995 | 3½" | £17 | $40 |

Goalkeeper Bunnykins™ Designer Denise Andrews
Limited edition of 250

116	1	1991	4½"	£85-£95	$145-$160
118	2	1991	4½"	£85-£95	$145-$160
120	3	1991	4½"	£85-£95	$145-$160
122	3	1991	4½"	£85-£95	$145-$160

Goodnight Bunnykins™ Designer Graham Tongue

| 157 | 1 | 1995-cur | 3½" | £14 | |

DB No	Version	Production Dates	Height	Market value	

Grandpa's Story Bunnykins™ Designer Walter Hayward

| 14 | 1 | 1974-1983 | 4″ | £350-£380 | $630-$650 |

Groom Bunnykins™ Designer Graham Tongue

| 102 | 1 | 1991-cur | 4½″ | £17 | $40 |

Guardsman Bunnykins™ Designer Denise Andrews   *picture page 67*
Limited edition of 1000

| 127 | 1 | 1992 | 4½″ | £80-£100 | $100-$120 |

Halloween Bunnykins™ Designer Graham Tongue

| 132 | 1 | 1993-cur | 3¼″ | £15-£20 | $25-$35 |

Happy Birthday Bunnykins™ Designer Harry Sales

| 21 | 1 | 1983-cur | 3¾″ | £17 | $40 |

Happy Birthday Bunnykins Music Box™ Designer Harry Sales

| 36 | 1 | 1984-1993 | 7″ | £60-£70 | $100-$120 |

Harry Bunnykins™ Designer Graham Tongue   *picture page 65*

| 73 | 1 | 1988-1993 | 3″ | £25-£35 | $40-$60 |

Harry The Herald™ Designer Harry Sales   *picture page 65, 66*

49	1	1986-1990	3½″	£40-£50	$70-$85
95	2	1990	3½″	£95-£105	$160-$180
115	3	1991	3½″	£440-£460	$750-$780

Home Run Bunnykins™ Designer Harry Sales   *picture page 59*

| 43 | 1 | 1986-1993 | 4″ | £30-£40 | $50-$70 |

Ice Cream Bunnykins™ Designer Graham Tongue   *picture page 62*

| 82 | 1 | 1990-1993 | 4½″ | £35-£40 | $60-$70 |

Jester Bunnykins™ Designer Denise Andrews
Limited edition of 1500

| 161 | 1 | 1995 | 4½″ | £45 | $85 |

DB No	Version	Production Dates	Height	Market value	

Jogging Bunnykins™ Designer Harry Sales   *picture page 60*

| 22 | 1 | 1983-1989 | 2½" | £60-£70 | $100-$120 |

Jogging Bunnykins Music Box™ Designer Harry Sales

| 37 | 1 | 1987-1989 | 5½" | £70-£80 | $120-$135 |

John Bull Bunnykins™ Designer Denise Andrews   *picture page 67*
Limited edition of 1000

| 134 | 1 | 1993 | 4½" | £100-£120 | $145-$160 |

King John™ Designer Harry Sales   *picture page 66*

| 45 | 1 | 1986-1990 | 4" | £30-£40 | $50-$70 |
| 91 | 2 | 1990 | 4" | £55-£65 | $95-$110 |

Knockout Bunnykins™ Designer Harry Sales

| 30 | 1 | 1985-1988 | 4" | £130-£150 | $180-$220 |

Lollipop Man Bunnykins™ Designer Graham Tongue *picture page 58*

| 65 | 1 | 1988-1991 | 3¾" | £80-£100 | $95-$110 |

Magician Bunnykins™ Designer Graham Tongue   *picture page 61*
Limited edition of 1000

| 126 | 1 | 1992 | 4½" | £85-£95 | $145-$160 |

Mary Bunnykins™ Designer Charles Noke   *picture page 69*

| 6002 | 1 | 1939-c1940 | 6½" | £1200-£1500 | $2050-$2550 |

Master Potter Bunnykins™ Designer Graham Tongue

| 131 | 1 | 1993 | 3¾" | £70-£80 | $120-$135 |

Milkman Bunnykins™ Designer Graham Tongue   *picture page 68*
Limited edition of 1000

| 125 | 1 | 1992 | 4½" | £80-£100 | $95-$110 |

Mother Bunnykins™ Designer Charles Noke   *picture page 69*

| 6004 | 1 | 1939-c1940s | 7" | £1200-£1500 | $2050-$2550 |

DB No	Version	Production Dates	Height	Market value	

Mother's Day Bunnykins™ Designer Shane Ridge

155	1	1995-cur	4″	£18	$40

Mr Bunnybeat Strumming™ Designer Harry Sales   *picture page 58*

16	1	1982-1988	4½″	£90-£100	$150-$170

Mr Bunnybeat Strumming Music Box™ Designer Harry Sales

38	1	1987-1989	7½″	£80-£90	$140-$150

Mr Bunnykins at the Easter Parade™ Designer Harry Sales *p59, p63*

18	1	1982-1993	5″	£20-£30	$35-$50
51	2	1986	5″	£340-£360	$580-$610

Mr Bunnykins Autumn Days™ Designer Walter Hayward   *p57*

5	1	1972-1982	4″	£290-£300	$460-$480

Mrs Bunnykins at the Easter Parade™ Designer Harry Sales   *p63*

19	1	1982	4½″	£17	$40
52	2	1986	4½″	£380-£400	$630-$650

Mrs Bunnykins at the Easter Parade Music Box™
Designer Harry Sales

39	1	1987-1991	7″	£60-£70	$100-$120

Mrs Bunnykins Clean Sweep™ Designer Walter Hayward   *p60*

6	1	1972-1991	4″	£50-£60	$85-$100

New Baby Bunnykins™ Designer Grahame Tongue

158	1	1995-cur	4″	£16	$40

Nurse Bunnykins™ Designer Graham Tongue

74	1	1989-1994	4¼″	£70-£80	$120-$140
74	2	1989-cur	4¼″	£14	$35

DB No	Version	Production Dates	Height		Market value

Olympic Bunnykins™ Designer Harry Sales   *picture page 60*

| 28 | 1 | 1984-1988 | 3¾" | £60-£70 | $100-$120 |
| 28 | 2 | 1984 | 3½" | £90-£100 | $150-$170 |

Out for a Duck™ Designer Denise Andrews
Limited edition of 1250

| 160 | 1 | 1995 | 4½" | £38 | $75 |

Paperboy Bunnykins™ Designer Graham Tongue   *picture page 59*

| 77 | 1 | 1989-1993 | 4" | £35-£40 | $60-$70 |

Partners in Collecting™ Designer Walter Hayward
See under Storytime Bunnykins

Policeman Bunnykins™ Designer Graham Tongue

| 64 | 1 | 1988 | 4¼" | £14 | $40 |

Polly Bunnykins™ Designer Graham Tongue   *picture page 62*

| 71 | 1 | 1988-1993 | 3½" | £25-£35 | $45-$60 |

Postman Bunnykins™ Designer Graham Tongue   *picture page 59*

| 76 | 1 | 1989-1993 | 4½" | £35-£45 | $60-$80 |

Prince Frederick™ Designer Harry Sales   *picture page 66*

| 48 | 1 | 1986-1990 | 3½" | £30-£40 | $50-$70 |
| 94 | 2 | 1990 | 3½" | £55-£65 | $95-$110 |

Princess Beatice™ Designer Harry Sales   *picture page 66*

| 93 | 2 | 1990 | 3½" | £55-£65 | $95-$110 |
| 47 | 1 | 1986-1990 | 3½" | £30-£40 | $50-$70 |

Queen Sophie™ Designer Harry Sales   *picture page 66*

| 46 | 1 | 1986-1990 | 4½" | £30-£40 | $50-$70 |
| 92 | 2 | 1990 | 4½" | £55-£65 | $95-$110 |

DB No	Version	Production Dates	Height	Market value	

Rainy Day Bunnykins™ Designer Graham Tongue

| 147 | 1 | 1994-cur | 4″ | £15 | $40 |

Reggie Bunnykins™ Designer Charles Noke *picture page 69*

| 6025 | 1 | 1939-c1940s | 3¾″ | £1580-£1800 | $2550-$3050 |

Rise and Shine Bunnykins™ Designer Walter Hayward *p57*

| 11 | 1 | 1973-1988 | 3¾″ | £120-£130 | $200-$220 |

Rock 'n' Roll Bunnykins™ Designer Harry Sales *picture page 62*
Limited edition of 1000

| 124 | 1 | 1991 | 4½″ | £90-£100 | $120-$140 |

Santa Bunnykins Happy Christmas™ Designer Harry Sales
No 62 is a limited edition Christmas Tree ornament

| 17 | 1 | 1981 | 4½″ | £17 | $40 |
| 62 | 1 | 1987 | | £600-£650 | $1100-$1125 |

Santa Bunnykins Music Box™ Designer Harry Sales

| 34 | 1 | 1984-1991 | 7¼″ | £60-£70 | $100-$120 |

Schoolboy Bunnykins™ Designer Graham Tongue

| 66 | 1 | 1988-1991 | 4″ | £90-£100 | $120-$140 |

Schooldays Bunnykins™ Designer Graham Tongue

| 57 | 1 | 1987-1994 | 3½″ | £10-£20 | $35-$45 |

Schoolmaster Bunnykins™ Designer Graham Tongue

| 60 | 1 | 1987-cur | 4″ | £15 | $40 |

Sergeant Mountie Bunnykins™ Designer Graham Tongue
Limited edition of 250

| 136 | 1 | 1993 | 4″ | £645-£655 | $1100-$1115 |

Sixtieth Anniversary of Bunnykins™ Designer Denise Andrews

| 137 | 1 | 1994 | 4½″ | £20-£30 | $35-$45 |

DB No	Version	Production Dates	Height	Market value	

Sleepytime™ Designer Walter Hayward

picture page 62

15	1	1974-1993	1¾"	£20-£30	$35-$50

Soccer Player Bunnykins™ Designer Denise Andrews
Limited edition of 250

picture page 68

123	4	1991	4½"	£85-£95	$145-$160

Sousaphone Bunnykins™ Designer Harry Sales

picture page 64

23	1	1984-1990	3½"	£30-£40	$50-$701
86	1	1990	3½"	£90-£110	$150-$190
105	1	1991	4"	£120-£130	$200-$220

Storytime Bunnykins™ Designer Walter Hayward
DB151 renamed **Partners in Collecting** colourway for US RDICC
15th anniversary

picture page 61

9	1	1972-cur	3"	£14	$35
59	2	1987	3"	£170-£180	$290-$300
151	3	1995	3"	£18	$45

Susan Bunnykins™ Designer Walter Hayward

picture page 59

70	1	1988-1993	3¼"	£25-£35	$40-$60

Susan Bunnykins as Queen of the May™
Designer Graham Tongue

picture page 65

83	1	1990-1991	4"	£30-£40	$50-$70

Sweetheart Bunnykins™ Designer Graham Tongue

130	1	1992-cur	3¾"	£15	$40

Tally Ho! Bunnykins™ Designer Walter Hayward

12	1	1973-1988	3¾"	£50-£60	$85-$100
78	2	1988	4"	£55-£65	$95-$110

Tally Ho! Music Box™ Designer Walter Hayward

33	1	1984-1993	7"	£60-£70	$100-$120
33	2	1988-1991	7"	£60-£70	$100-$120

DB No	Version	Production Dates	Height	Market value	

The Artist™ Designer Walter Hayward

13	1	1974-1982	3¾″	£370-£380	$630-$650

Tom Bunnykins™ Designer Graham Tongue   *picture page 62*

72	1	1988-1993	3″	£25-£35	$45-$60

Touchdown Bunnykins™ Designer Harry Sales   *picture page 60, 65*
DB96-100 inclusive were issued as a limited edition of 200

29	1	1985-1988	3¼″	£60-£70	$100-$120
29	2	1985	3¼″	£440-£460	$750-$780
96	3	1990	3¼″	£120-£130	$200-$220
97	4	1990	3¼″	£120-£130	$200-$220
98	5	1990	3¼″	£120-£130	$200-$220
99	6	1990	3¼″	£120-£130	$200-$220
100	7	1990	3½″	£120-£130	$200-$220

Trumpeter Bunnykins™ Designer Harry Sales
DB106 was issued as a limited edition of 300

24	1	1984-1990	3½″	£30-£40	$50-$70
87	1	1990	3¾″	£90-£110	$150-$190
106	1	1991	3¾″	£120-£130	$200-$220

Uncle Sam Bunnykins™ Designer Harry Sales
USA only

50	1	1986-cur	4½″	£35-£45	$60-$80

Wicket Keeper™ Designer Denise Andrews   *picture page 68*
Limited edition of 1000

150	1	1994	3½″	£60-£80	

William Bunnykins™ Designer Walter Hayward   *picture page 61*

69	1	1988-1993	3¾″	£30-£40	$50-$70

THE BEST DOULTON
GOES TO PHILLIPS

The Bunnykins family
Left to right, Freddie, sold for £2,400; Reggie, sold for £2,200; Farmer, sold for £2,000,
Mary, sold for £2,000; Mother, (r. to ears) sold for £700 and Billy, sold for £2,000

Phillips hold specialised auctions of Doulton Ware each a year in May and October, to coinside with the major Doulton Fairs.

To discuss selling your Doulton at auction through Phillips please contact Mark Oliver on (0171) 629 6602, ext 233

LONDON

Phillips
INTERNATIONAL
AUCTIONEERS & VALUERS

101 New Bond Street, London W1Y 0AS

Doulton & Beswick

"Jester" Bunnykins DB161

Exclusive limited edtion of 1500 from UKI Ceramics Ltd
For further information write or call
Zoe Gillian, Product Manager, UK International Ceramics Ltd
10 Wilford Bridge Spur, Melton, Woodbridge, Suffolk IP12 1RJ UK
Tel: 01394 386662 Fax: 01394 386742

"Out for a Duck" Bunnykins DB161

Exclusive limited edtion of 1250 from UKI Ceramics Ltd
For further information write or call
Zoe Gillian, Product Manager, UK International Ceramics Ltd
10 Wilford Bridge Spur, Melton, Woodbridge, Suffolk IP12 1RJ UK
Tel: 01394 386662 Fax: 01394 386742

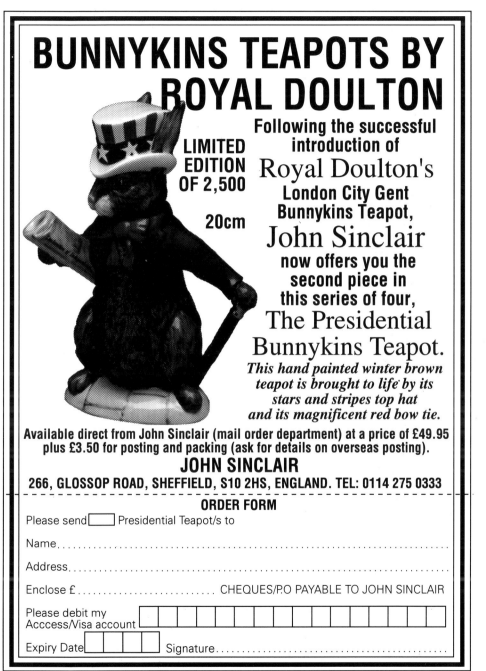